SNOOPY STARS
AS
THE FLYING ACE

Charles M. Schulz

RAVETTE BOOKS

This edition first published by
Ravette Books Limited 1988

Printed and bound in Great Britain
for Ravette Books Limited,
3 Glenside Estate, Star Road, Partridge Green,
Horsham, Sussex RH13 8RA
by Cox & Wyman Ltd, Reading

ISBN 1 85304 026 6

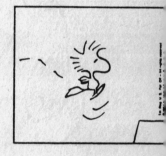

PEANUTS

WHY ARE YOU EATING SO FAST?

RIGHT AFTER DINNER I'M GOING INTO WAFFLETOWN TO THE BALL GAME

6-20

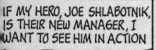

IF MY HERO, JOE SHLABOTNIK, IS THEIR NEW MANAGER, I WANT TO SEE HIM IN ACTION

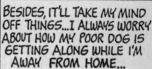

BESIDES, IT'LL TAKE MY MIND OFF THINGS...I ALWAYS WORRY ABOUT HOW MY POOR DOG IS GETTING ALONG WHILE I'M AWAY FROM HOME...

OKAY, SNOOPY, IT'S A DEAL! MARCIE AND I WILL RENT YOUR SOPWITH CAMEL FROM YOU FOR ONE DOLLAR!

SCHULZ

PEANUTS

THERE IT IS, MARCIE! THERE'S THE PLANE YOU AND I WILL BE FLYING IN THE POWDER PUFF DERBY!

IT'S A BEAUTY, GIR

IT HAS A ONE HUNDRED AND FIFTY HORSEPOWER ENGINE, AND IT CARRIES THIRTY-SEVEN GALLONS OF GAS

6-24

OH, HEY, MECHANIC! I WAS GOING TO ASK YOU...HOW ABOUT REMOVING THE MACHINE GUNS?

WE RARELY USE MACHINE GUNS IN THE POWDER PUFF DERBY! HA HA HA HA!!

STRANGE GIRL! WEIRD SENSE OF HUMOR...

PEANUTS

SIR, I HAVE A QUESTION..

HOW ARE WE GOING TO FIND OUR WAY FROM RIVERSIDE, CALIFORNIA, TO BOYNE FALLS, MICHIGAN, WHEN WE FLY IN THE POWDER PUFF DERBY?

6-26

WE'LL USE A MAP! WHAT DID YOU THINK WE'D DO?

I WAS AFRAID WE WERE GOING TO FLY BY THE SEAT OF YOUR PANTS, SIR...

DON'T BE VULGAR, MARCIE!

PEANUTS

WHEN DOES THE POWDER PUFF DERBY BEGIN, SIR?

WE CAN'T LEAVE UNTIL THE MAN FROM THE CHAMBER OF COMMERCE GETS HERE...

7-2

MMMMM! SMAK!SMAK! SMAK!SMAK! ♡♡♡♡

DON'T SLUG HIM MARCIE..WE MIGHT GET DISQUALIFIED!

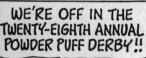

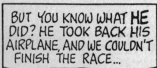

THINGS HAVE REALLY CHANGED, CHARLIE BROWN..

NO ONE SEEMS TO HAVE A SENSE OF ADVENTURE ANY MORE...

4-20

CHOP
CHOP
CHOP
CHOP

WELL, ALMOST NO ONE...

SCHULZ

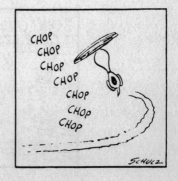

1-30

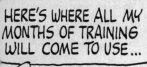

HERE'S THE WORLD WAR I FLYING ACE SOARING OVER THE FRONT LINES IN HIS SOPWITH CAMEL...

2-3

HE WAVES TO THE POOR BLIGHTERS IN THE TRENCHES BELOW

IN THEIR ADMIRATION FOR HIM THEY SHOWER HIM WITH GIFTS...

LIKE ROCKS!

SCHULZ

HERE'S THE WORLD WAR I FLYING ACE STROLLING DOWN A COUNTRY ROAD...ONCE AGAIN HE SEES THE CHARMING FRENCH LASS..

QUICKLY HE CONSULTS HIS PHRASE BOOK... "I AM HAPPY TO MEET YOU"

ENCHANTÉ DE FAIRE VOTRE CONNAISSANCE

SIGH

SCHULZ

2-6

HERE'S THE WORLD WAR I FLYING ACE SITTING IN A LITTLE CAFE...ONCE AGAIN HE IS DEPRESSED...

HIS LEAVE IS OVER, AND HE HAS FAILED TO MEET THE CHARMING FRENCH LASS...

HE DECIDES TO FORGET HER BY DRINKING ROOT BEER...GARÇON! ANOTHER ROUND, S'IL VOUS PLAÎT!

UNFORTUNATELY, IT'S VERY HARD TO FORGET ANYONE BY DRINKING ROOT BEER!

2-10

HERE'S THE WORLD WAR I FLYING ACE DOWN BEHIND ENEMY LINES WEARING ONE OF HIS FAMOUS DISGUISES

"C MINUS"?!!

I WORK ALL NIGHT ON A PAPER, AND ALL I GET IS A "C MINUS"!

© 1979 United Feature Syndicate, Inc.

3-29

REALLY? WHY, THANK YOU...IT IS QUITE BEAUTIFUL, ISN'T IT?

5-14

HE SAID I HAVE A NICE SKY

© 1979 United Feature Syndicate, Inc.

HERE'S THE WORLD WAR I FLYING ACE IN PARIS...

HE IS SITTING IN A SMALL SIDEWALK CAFE WITH A BEAUTIFUL YOUNG FRENCH LASS...

HE MUST IMPRESS HER WITH HIS SOPHISTICATED MANNER

MAY I SEE THE ROOT BEER LIST, PLEASE?

© 1980 United Feature Syndicate, Inc.

6-5

GOOD AFTERNOON, LADIES AND GENTLEMEN..WE ARE ABOUT TO SERVE LUNCH..

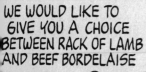

WE WOULD LIKE TO GIVE YOU A CHOICE BETWEEN RACK OF LAMB AND BEEF BORDELAISE

BUT WE CAN'T

© 1980 United Feature Syndicate, Inc.

SO HOW ABOUT A BANANA?

© 1980 United Feature Syndicate, Inc.   8-12

THIS HIGHWAY
PATROLLED BY
AIRCRAFT

HERE'S THE WORLD WAR I FLYING ACE HANGING AROUND THE BARRACKS...

10-4

HE IS RESTLESS..THERE IS NOTHING TO DO EXCEPT PLAY CARDS...

OKAY, MEN, THE GAME IS "PIG"! IF YOU GET TWO OF A KIND, YOU PUT YOUR FINGER AGAINST YOUR NOSE LIKE THIS...GOT IT?

ACTUALLY, FLYING ACES VERY SELDOM PLAYED "PIG"

8

YES, SIR, I THINK I KNOW WHY YOU PUT ALL THESE WIRES ON MY HEAD...

9-23

AFTER I FALL ASLEEP, YOU CAN TELL IF I'M NARCOLEPTIC IF MY "RAPID EYE MOVEMENT" BEGINS RIGHT AWAY...

INCIDENTALLY, HOW IS MY FRIEND, SNOOPY, DOING IN THE NEXT ROOM?

© 1983 United Feature Syndicate. Inc.

HERE'S THE WORLD WAR I FLYING ACE BEING TORTURED BY THE ENEMY...

3-16

© 1984 United Feature Syndicate, Inc.

YES, MA'AM...UNDER HERE, I'M HERE!

3-17

HERE'S THE WORLD FAMOUS DIVER ABOUT TO PERFORM HIS FANTASTIC FORWARD RUNNING DIVE...

8-17 © 1984 United Feature Syndicate, Inc.

DON'T YOU DARE!

FOLLOWED BY HIS "KEEP GOING AND PROBABLY LAND ON HIS HEAD" DIVE!

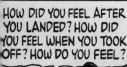

7-27

I DON'T KNOW WHAT IT IS, BUT I CAUGHT IT!

Other Snoopy titles published by Ravette Books

All these books are available at your local bookshop or news-agent, or can be ordered direct from the publisher. Just tick the titles you require and fill in the form below. Prices and availability subject to change without notice.

Ravette Books Limited, 3 Glenside Estate, Star Road, Partridge Green, Horsham, West Sussex RH13 8RA

Please send a cheque or postal order, and allow the following for postage and packing. UK: 45p for one book plus 30p for each additional book.

Name ....

Address ....

....